CYBERSPACE

Contents

Glossary

Before you read the book, do you know what these words mean?

cyberspace

A place where computer information lives.

dataglove

A glove that a person wears that is connected to a computer to measure hand movement.

datasuit

A suit that a person wears that is connected to a computer to measure body movement.

flight simulator

A machine or computer that people can use to learn about flying without using a plane.

hologram

A special photograph made by laser light.

scanner

A machine that takes a picture of something onto a computer.

virtual reality

An imaginary world made with computers that lets you feel as if you are a part of it.

Here are some Internet sites that you could visit:

The CyberSpace Middle School
http://hillside.coled.umn.edu/

Freezone
http://freezone.com/

KIDLINK
http://www.kidlink.org/

The Computer Museum
http://www.net.org/

The Super-Duper Word-Eating Computer

Written by Kate Breheny Illustrated by Lance Ross

Webster's mother bought herself a new computer for her birthday. The old one came to live in Webster's room.

"There's nothing wrong with it," Webster's mother said. "It's just a little old."

The old computer sat on the desk and stared. "Stop staring, you stupid old thing," said Webster.

Webster did not look at the old computer. It kept on staring. At last, Webster took a shirt and put it over the computer's face.

"So there, old Ugly," Webster laughed.

Soon, the old computer was piled high with dirty socks and clothes. On the top, Webster added a hat and sunglasses.

Soon, Webster forgot that the old computer was there at all. He kept adding to the pile until it reached up to the roof.

"Clean your room, Webster!" his mother yelled one night.

Webster grumbled but started to clear his things away. That was when he saw that something strange had been going on. Certain words were missing from books. Certain words had gone off posters and out of comics. Certain words had even gone from some of his clothes.

Which words do you think had gone from Webster's books?

5

Webster looked about his room. First he found that the things nearest to the old computer had the most gaps where words had been. Then he saw that all the words that had gone were "food" words. The old computer had been eating words!

Webster threw the dirty socks and clothes and books on the floor. For the first time, he turned on the old computer.

The blank screen lit up like one big blue eye. Webster gulped then began to type.

Sandwich, he typed in the middle of the screen. For a moment nothing happened. Then with a quiet gulp, the word disappeared. Webster's mouth dropped open. Then he typed in another word.

Broccoli, he typed. Nothing happened at all. The word stayed in the middle of the screen.

Webster tried some more words. *Hamburger*, he typed. As soon as the word was typed, it disappeared.

It was the same with *Chocolate, chocolate cake,* and *chocolate ice cream.* Webster laughed as he typed in *spinach,* but that stayed on the screen with *broccoli.* He tried *banana,* and after a minute the word was eaten.

Webster laughed out loud. "Cool," he said. "It's a super-duper word-eating computer!" He started looking through the piles of clothes and books to find out which other words the computer liked.

cake banana cream burger fudge pizza apple pie bacon

"Is your room clean yet, Webster?" asked his mother.

Webster came out with a pile of dirty clothes. "I've just found out that the old computer eats words," he said. "I'm going to make up a menu for it."

"Don't forget the green vegetables," his mother said. "Webster, what on earth did you do to your clothes? I'm sure this T-shirt used to say *Chip off the old block*. What happened to the *Chip*?"

"The computer must have eaten it," said Webster. "It likes chips."

Webster figured out a menu for his computer that kept it from eating words out of his room. Thinking about what his mother had said, he always typed in the vegetables first. *Broccoli* always went before *steak*. *Spinach* always went before *pizza*. Webster wouldn't type in the next food if the vegetables weren't eaten. If the old computer ate up its vegetables, Webster always ended with a nice dessert: *apple pie, gingersnaps, hot fudge sundae*.

Webster was so busy with his computer that the school year ended in no time.

"You're staying with your Aunt Mary for a while," his mother said. "Can you tear yourself away from your room for a week?"

"Only if you feed the computer," Webster said.

Webster wrote a list for his mother and taped it to the computer screen. "Don't forget to feed me," it said. Underneath there was a menu for every day that he would be away. Webster's mother smiled as she saw the note, but then she firmly closed Webster's door.

Three days passed, then four, then five. On the last day, Aunt Mary brought Webster home.

"I'm home," he yelled as he came into the kitchen.

A strange sight greeted Webster. His mother was sitting on the floor with all her recipe books open. She was turning page after page.

"What's up?" asked Webster.

"I wanted to do some baking," said his mother. "But look, all of the food words have gone out of the cookbooks. They're full of gaps."

Sure enough, all the food words were missing from the recipes, even down to *flour* and *sugar*. Well, almost all the food words had gone, except for anything green, like *broccoli*, and *spinach*.

Webster gulped. "You didn't feed the computer, did you?" he said to his mother.

Soon the signs were everywhere that Webster's computer had been eating all the food words in the place. *Cakes* and *chocolate fudge brownies* were gone from magazines on the coffee table. Names like *Bacon, Sweet,* and *Candy* were even missing from the telephone book.

Webster went to his room and opened the door. The old computer was so big it was almost breaking the desk.

cake banana cream burger fudge pizza apple pie bacon

Webster knew what he had to do. He turned the old computer on. The screen lit up, a bright purple. Slowly, Webster typed in *broccoli.*

After that, it was as if a tornado had been let loose in Webster's home. All the words that had been eaten burst out, all over the walls and the ceilings, all over clothes and pictures. Some of them even landed with a plop back inside the recipe books.

When it was over, Webster moved away. The old computer was looking very small and very sick. Its screen was glowing a pale green.

"Serves you right, you greedy thing," said Webster.

Food was always very different from that day on in Webster's home. Webster and his mother could never really sort out which words went where. Webster didn't mind eating up chicken noodle pie, and bacon-and-egg ice cream anyway.

The best part was feeding the old computer the new recipes out of the recipe books. Webster laughed as he typed in spinach burger, and broccoli chips, and hot cabbage cake.

But sometimes the old computer nibbled words like *chocolate* out of books and off posters, out of comics and off Webster's clothes. Just as a warning. . .

Virtual Reality

Written by Anne Sinclair

Have you ever wished you could be part of a story from a film or book you like? You could be the hero of a science-fiction story or a wild adventure. You could see how it feels to fly a spaceship, or drive a race car, or fly a plane. You can do all these things using virtual reality.

Virtual reality is a world made by a computer. The computer makes a new world, and you feel as if you are part of the action in this new world. Virtual reality lets you race cars on famous racetracks or play golf on famous courses.

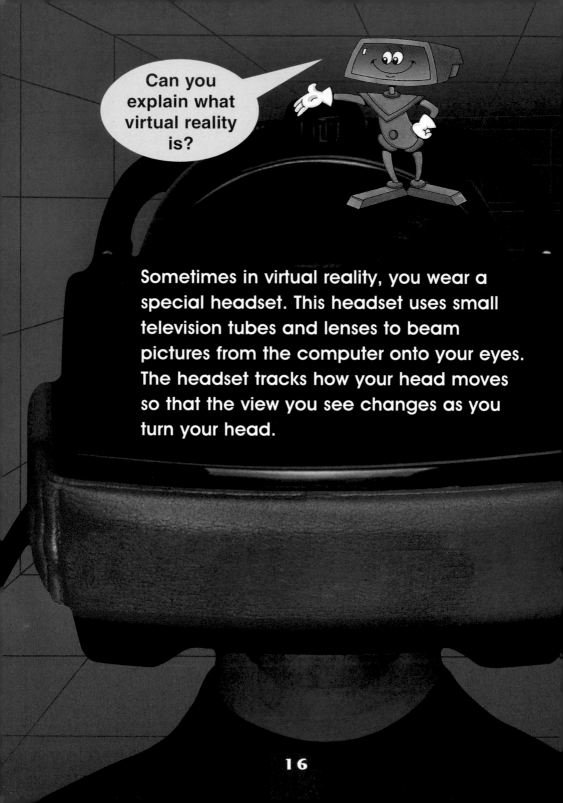

Can you explain what virtual reality is?

Sometimes in virtual reality, you wear a special headset. This headset uses small television tubes and lenses to beam pictures from the computer onto your eyes. The headset tracks how your head moves so that the view you see changes as you turn your head.

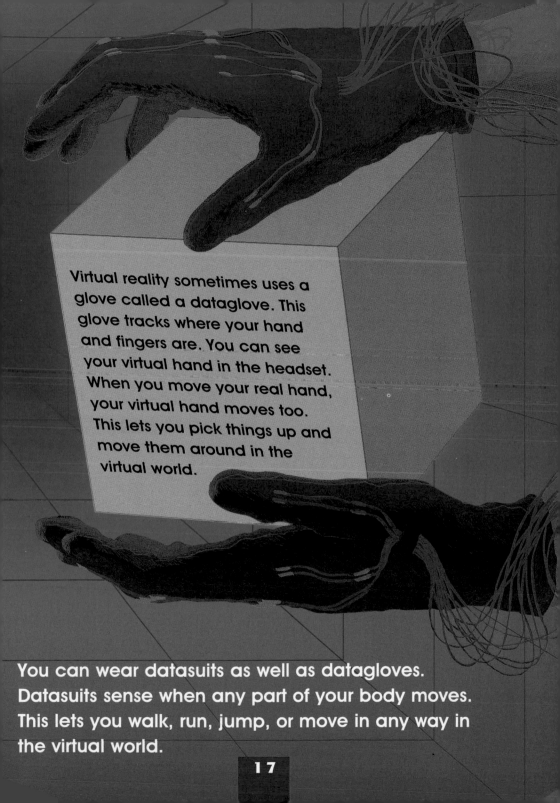

Virtual reality sometimes uses a glove called a dataglove. This glove tracks where your hand and fingers are. You can see your virtual hand in the headset. When you move your real hand, your virtual hand moves too. This lets you pick things up and move them around in the virtual world.

You can wear datasuits as well as datagloves. Datasuits sense when any part of your body moves. This lets you walk, run, jump, or move in any way in the virtual world.

Virtual reality lets you play games that are lots of fun and seem very real. Virtual reality can do a lot more than that, too. It will become more and more important for training people. Even now, pilots learn how to fly planes on flight simulators that use virtual reality. Medical students will be able to learn to operate on patients in virtual reality. Firefighters will learn to fight dangerous fires in virtual reality. Any job that is dangerous or expensive could use virtual reality for training.

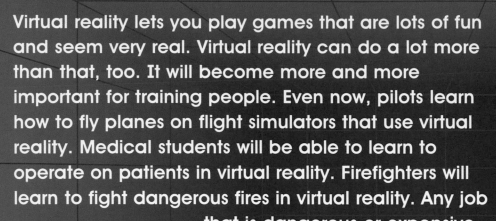

In schools, students could learn about history by taking part in virtual reality. Students could learn about science by going inside a space shuttle or inside the human body in virtual reality.

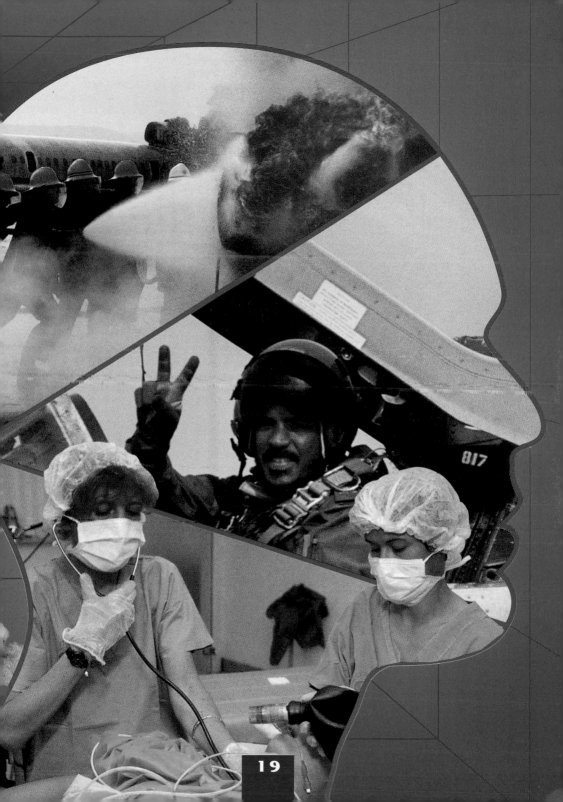

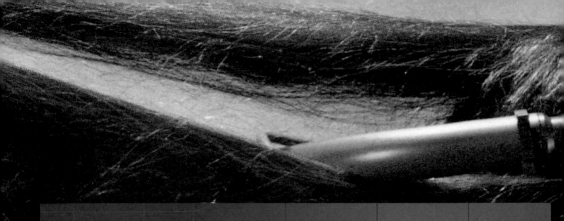

Virtual reality is getting better all the time. At the moment, the things that we see in virtual reality don't look very real. People are working to make them better and faster. Virtual reality will become even more real in the future. Right now, you can only see and hear things in virtual reality. One day you will be able to feel, smell, and taste things, too. All your senses will be used.

But virtual reality could also have some bad effects. Some people think that you might lose touch with the real world if you spend too much time in virtual reality. In virtual reality, people can take part in violent adventures and no one really gets hurt. Could this affect the way they behave in the real world? Some people said the same thing about television when it was invented.

What do you think?

Cyberfuture

Written by Elizabeth Hookings and Kristie Rogers
Illustrated by Fraser Williamson

What's life going to be like in the future?
Will computers control our lives?
Will robots be able to think?

Meet Alka. She's from the future.

Hi! Welcome to my home. I live here with my mother and father and my big brother.

Zara, our computer, lets me in and out of the house when she hears my voice. She also turns the lights on and off to save the solar power when we go in and out of rooms. In fact, she looks after everyone and everything in the house. You can't see Zara, but you can talk to her. She's everywhere inside.

Zara controls AI, our robot. Zara tells AI when the plants need watering, when the rooms need to be cleaned, and what to cook for dinner. In fact, Zara tells AI everything.

Every day, I put my hand in this scanner and Zara figures out the vitamins and other things I need. Then she tells AI what to cook for each meal. My dad is old-fashioned. He likes to do the cooking sometimes as a hobby. He's not as good a cook as AI, but he says it helps him relax.

Zara orders more food as soon as the food we have gets used up. Sometimes, when Dad wants to cook, he and I go to the cybermart for fun. We go into the holosuite and visit the supermarket. We can walk up and down the rows, pick up the fruits and vegetables, and smell them. We can even have a virtual taste if we want. Then we just push a button and everything we have chosen gets sent to us an hour or so later. I can't imagine what it used to be like when people had to go to a real supermarket and try to find a place to park those big old cars that polluted the air. And imagine having to stand in line to buy something!

We also use the holosuite to visit other places. The places I like to visit most are the other planets in the solar system. I like going to Egypt and Africa, too. Sometimes we really go to other places for a week or two.
It's fun. But the problem is you spend too much time getting there.

I spend a lot of time in the holosuite, because this is where I go to school. My teacher is Miss Evans. There are fifty of us in our cyberclass. Miss Evans is pretty strict, but I guess she's OK. We're learning about the human body at the moment. We all shrank ourselves right down until we were tiny, and then we went all around inside a body. It was fun visiting the heart.

Do you have your own hologram phone? I like it
because when my parents go away, I can still talk to
them and see them as if they were here. I can also see
what they are seeing, so I can take a look at the place
they are visiting. I talk to my friend Rabina in Sri Lanka
on the holophone as well. One day, I want to visit her
in real life.

This is our HTV. It's not the latest model like Amy's, but I think it's OK. I like to watch basketball games. It feels like you are really at the game, in the crowd. But you can also replay a shot or zoom in close as if you were one of the players whenever you want.

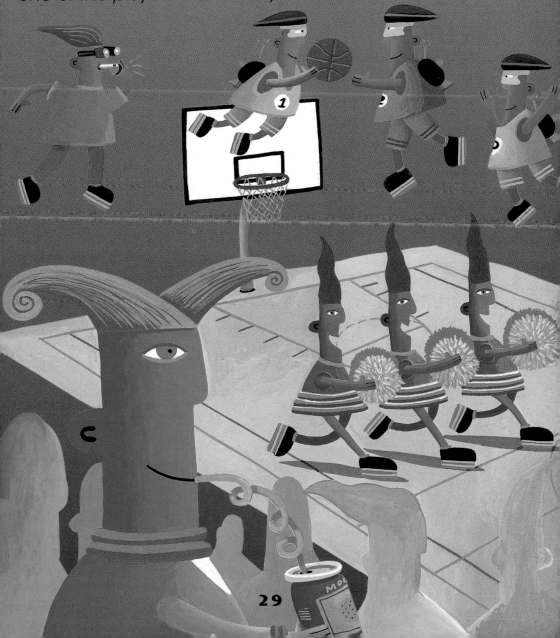

This is my bedroom. I had it set up like Cleopatra's room last night. The night before, I had it set up as if I was asleep under the stars in a forest. The trouble is, I lay awake watching all the stars and the animals. One of the best ways of having my bedroom is as if it is on a boat. Then it feels all warm, and I get rocked to sleep by the waves. Tonight I might mix it all up and see what happens!

So what's your house like? Can I come and visit you some day?

Leopard

Index